First published in the United Kingdom in 2002 by
The Chicken House, 2 Palmer Street, Frome,
Somerset BA11 1DS

Designed by Tracey Cunnell

Printed in Dubai by Oriental Press

British Library Cataloguing in Publication data available.
Library of Congress Cataloguing in Publication data available.

ISBN: 1 903434 35 1

The Children's Book of
ALPHABETS

Introduction by Wendy Cooling

A Was Once an Apple Pie
Illustrated by Rosalind Beardshaw

The Shaker Abecedarius
Illustrated by Jan Barger

A Was an Archer
Illustrated by Tiphanie Beeke

An Alphabet of Nursery Rhymes
Illustrated by Lynne Chapman

The Christmas Alphabet
Illustrated by Mary Claire Smith

The Chicken House

The Children's Book of Alphabets

This collection of alphabets celebrates the importance of language and art in the education of children. The alphabet has long been a starting point of the child's journey into reading, and its presentation has been enhanced by the creative use of words and pictures from the days of chanting and rote learning to the present day. The alphabets in this book illustrate a wish to make learning fun for the very young.

The first alphabet, with its amazing words that are a joy to read aloud, offers a wonderful introduction to the nonsense world of Edward Lear. The strength of the rhyme and rhythm invites children to predict the next verse, and so develop an important pre-reading skill in a fun and entertaining way.

The Shaker Abecedarius teaches and entertains. The language fascinates from the moment the young reader concentrates on pronouncing 'abecedarius', and continues through the rhyming and rhythm of the list of extraordinary animals, such as the bobolink and the whippoorwill – words chosen for the wonder of their sounds.

A Was an Archer, the oldest alphabet in the collection, offers intriguing images of a past world. It shows us that the art of giving life to the alphabet is not easy: enjoy the way it deals with the ever-challenging 'X'.

The two modern alphabets demonstrate the endless possibilities and make it clear that alphabet books will be written for years to come. *An Alphabet of Nursery Rhymes* presents a collection of rhymes for every family and introduces another way into reading and language learning. *The Christmas Alphabet* celebrates a child-centred festival – its simple word approach will encourage children to make their own alphabet books. For the alphabet is owned by and is accessible to everyone!

Wendy Cooling 2002

A Was Once an Apple Pie

Edward Lear

Illustrated by Rosalind Beardshaw

A was once an apple pie,
Pidy,
Widy,
Tidy,
Pidy,
Nice insidy,
Applie-pie!

B was once a little bear,
Beary,
Wary,
Hairy,
Beary,
Taky cary,
Little bear!

a
b
c
d
e
f
g
h
i
j
k
l
m
n
o
p
q
r
s
t
u
v
w
x
y
z

C was once a little cake,
Caky,
Baky,
Maky,
Caky,
Taky caky
Little cake!

D was once a little doll,
Dolly,
Molly,
Polly,
Nolly,
Nursy dolly,
Little doll!

a
b
c
d
e
f
g
h
i
j
k
l
m
n
o
p
q
r
s
t
u
v
w
x
y
z

E was once a little eel,
Eely,
Weely,
Peely,
Eely,
Twirly, tweely,
Little eel!

F was once a little fish,
Fishy,
Wishy,
Squishy,
Fishy,
In a dishy,
Little fish!

G was once a little goose,
　　　Goosy,
　　　Moosy,
　　　Boosy,
　　　Goosy,
　　　Waddly-woosy,
　　　Little goose!

H was once a little hen,
　　　Henny,
　　　Chenny,
　　　Tenny,
　　　Henny,
　　　Eggsy-any,
　　　Little hen?

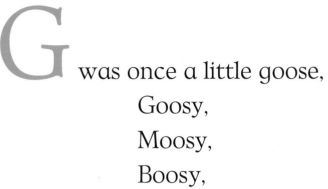

11

a b c d e f g h i j k l m n o p q r s t u v w x y z

I was once a bottle of ink,
Inky,
Dinky,
Thinky,
Inky,
Blacky minky,
Bottle of ink!

J was once a jar of jam,
Jammy,
Mammy,
Clammy,
Jammy,
Sweety, swammy,
Jar of jam!

K was once a little kite,
Kity,
Whity,
Flighty,
Kity,
Out of sighty,
Little kite!

L was once a little lark,
Larky,
Marky,
Harky,
Larky,
In the parky,
Little lark!

a
b
c
d
e
f
g
h
i
j
k
l
m
n
o
p
q
r
s
t
u
v
w
x
y
z

M was once a little mouse,
Mousy,
Bousy,
Sousy,
Mousy,
In the housy,
Little mouse!

N was once a little needle,
Needly,
Tweedly,
Threedly,
Needly,
Wisky, wheedly,
Little needle!

O was once a little owl,
   Owly,
   Prowly,
   Howly,
   Owly,
   Browny fowly,
   Little owl!

P was once a little pump,
   Pumpy,
   Slumpy,
   Flumpy,
   Pumpy,
   Dumpy, thumpy,
   Little pump!

Q was once a little quail,
Quaily,
Faily,
Daily,
Quaily,
Stumpy-taily,
Little quail!

R was once a little rose,
Rosy,
Posy,
Nosy,
Rosy,
Blows-y, grows-y,
Little rose!

S was once a little shrimp,
   Shrimpy,
   Nimpy,
   Flimpy,
   Shrimpy,
   Jumpy, jimpy,
   Little shrimp!

T was once a little thrush,
   Thrushy,
   Hushy,
   Bushy,
   Thrushy,
   Flitty, flushy,
   Little thrush!

17

a b c d e f g h i j k l m n o p q r s t u v w x y z

U was once a little urn,
Urny,
Burny,
Turny,
Urny,
Bubbly, burny,
Little urn!

V was once a little vine,
Viny,
Winy,
Twiny,
Viny,
Twisty-twiny,
Little vine!

W was once a whale,
Whaly,
Scaly,
Shaly,
Whaly,
Tumbly-taily,
Mighty whale!

X was once a great king Xerxes,
Xerxy,
Perxy,
Turxy,
Xerxy,
Linxy, lurxy,
Great King Xerxes!

19

a
b
c
d
e
f
g
h
i
j
k
l
m
n
o
p
q
r
s
t
u
v
w
x
y
z

Y was once a little yew,
Yewdy,
Fewdy,
Crudy,
Yewdy,
Growdy, grewdy,
Little yew!

Z was once a piece of zinc,
Tinky,
Winky,
Blinky,
Tinky,
Tinky, minky,
Piece of zinc!

The Shaker Abecedarius

From **The Shaker Manifesto, 1882**

Illustrated by Jan Barger

a
b
c
d
e
f
g
h
i
j
k
l
m
n
o
p
q
r
s
t
u
v
w
x
y
z

Alligator,
beetle,
porcupine,
whale,

Bobolink,
panther,
dragonfly,
snail,

a
b
c
d
e
f
g
h
i
j
k
l
m
n
o
p
q
r
s
t
u
v
w
x
y
z

23

rocodile,
monkey,
buffalo,
hare,

a b c d e f g h i j k l m n o p q r s t u v w x y z

Dromedary,
leopard,
mud turtle,
bear,

E lephant,
badger,
pelican,
ox,

a b c d e f g h i j k l m n o p q r s t u v w x y z

Flying Fish, reindeer, anaconda, fox,

27

a b c d e f g h i j k l m n o p q r s t u v w x y z

Guinea pig,
dolphin,
antelope,
goose,

28

Hummingbird, weasel, pickerel, moose,

29

a
b
c
d
e
f
g
h
i
j
k
l
m
n
o
p
q
r
s
t
u
v
w
x
y
z

Ibex,
rhinoceros,
owl,
kangaroo,

Jackal, opossum, toad, cockatoo,

a b c d e f g h i j k l m n o p q r s t u v w x y z

a b c d e f g h i j k l m n o p q r s t u v w x y z

Kingfisher,
peacock,
anteater,
bat,

Lizard,
ichneumon,
honeybee,
rat,

33

a
b
c
d
e
f
g
h
i
j
k
l
m
n
o
p
q
r
s
t
u
v
w
x
y
z

Mockingbird, camel, grasshopper, mouse,

Nightingale,
spider,
cuttlefish,
grouse,

a
b
c
d
e
f
g
h
i
j
k
l
m
n
o
p
q
r
s
t
u
v
w
x
y
z

a b c d e f g h i j k l m n o p q r s t u v w x y z

Ocelot,
pheasant,
wolverine,
auk,

P eriwinkle,
ermine,
katydid,
hawk,

a b c d e f g h i j k l m n o p q r s t u v w x y z

a b c d e f g h i j k l m n o p q r s t u v w x y z

Quail,
hippopotamus,
armadillo,
moth,

Rattlesnake,
lion,
woodpecker,
sloth,

a
b
c
d
e
f
g
h
i
j
k
l
m
n
o
p
q
r
s
t
u
v
w
x
y
z

S alamander, goldfinch, angleworm, dog,

40

Tiger,
flamingo,
scorpion,
frog,

a
b
c
d
e
f
g
h
i
j
k
l
m
n
o
p
q
r
s
t
u
v
w
x
y
z

Unicorn,
ostrich,
nautilus,
mole,

42

Viper,
gorilla,
basilisk,
sole,

a
b
c
d
e
f
g
h
i
j
k
l
m
n
o
p
q
r
s
t
u
v
w
x
y
z

W

hippoorwill,
beaver,
centipede,
fawn,

Xanthos,
canary,
polliwog,
swan,

a
b
c
d
e
f
g
h
i
j
k
l
m
n
o
p
q
r
s
t
u
v
w
x
y
z

a
b
c
d
e
f
g
h
i
j
k
l
m
n
o
p
q
r
s
t
u
v
w
x
y
z

Yellowhammer,
eagle,
hyena,
lark,

Zebra,
chameleon,
butterfly,
shark.

a
b
c
d
e
f
g
h
i
j
k
l
m
n
o
p
q
r
s
t
u
v
w
x
y
z

The Shaker Abecedarius

From *The Shaker Manifesto, 1882*

Alligator, Beetle, Porcupine, Whale,
Bobolink, Panther, Dragonfly, Snail,
Crocodile, Monkey, Buffalo, Hare,
Dromedary, Leopard, Mud Turtle, Bear,
Elephant, Badger, Pelican, Ox,
Flying Fish, Reindeer, Anaconda, Fox,
Guinea Pig, Dolphin, Antelope, Goose,
Hummingbird, Weasel, Pickerel, Moose,
Ibex, Rhinoceros, Owl, Kangaroo,
Jackal, Opossum, Toad, Cockatoo,
Kingfisher, Peacock, Anteater, Bat,
Lizard, Ichneumon, Honeybee, Rat,
Mockingbird, Camel, Grasshopper, Mouse,
Nightingale, Spider, Cuttlefish, Grouse,
Ocelot, Pheasant, Wolverine, Auk,
Periwinkle, Ermine, Katydid, Hawk,
Quail, Hippopotamus, Armadillo, Moth,
Rattlesnake, Lion, Woodpecker, Sloth,
Salamander, Goldfinch, Angleworm, Dog,
Tiger, Flamingo, Scorpion, Frog,
Unicorn, Ostrich, Nautilus, Mole,
Viper, Gorilla, Basilisk, Sole,
Whippoorwill, Beaver, Centipede, Fawn,
Xanthos, Canary, Polliwog, Swan,
Yellowhammer, Eagle, Hyena, Lark,
Zebra, Chameleon, Butterfly, Shark.

A Was an Archer

From Tom Thumb's Picture Alphabet

Illustrated by Tiphanie Beeke

A was an Archer,
and shot at a frog;

B was a Butcher,
and had a great dog.

C was a Captain,
all covered with lace;

D was a Drummer,
    and had a red face.

E was an Esquire,
    with pride on his brow;

F was a Farmer,
    and followed the plough.

a
b
c
d
e
f
g
h
i
j
k
l
m
n
o
p
q
r
s
t
u
v
w
x
y
z

G was a Gamester,
   who had but ill luck;

H was a Hunter,
   and hunted a buck.

I was an Innkeeper,
   who loved to carouse;

J was a Joiner,
   and built up a house.

K was a King,
   so mighty and grand;

L was a Lady,
   who had a white hand.

a
b
c
d
e
f
g
h
i
j
k
l
m
n
o
p
q
r
s
t
u
v
w
x
y
z

M was a Miser,
   and hoarded up gold;

N was a Nobleman,
   gallant and bold.

O was an Oyster wench,
and went about town;

P was a Parson,
and wore a black gown.

Q was a Queen,
who was fond of good flip;

R was a Robber,
and wanted a whip.

S was a Sailor,
   who spent all he got;

T was a Tinker,
   who mended a pot.

U was an Usurer,
   a miserable elf;

V was a Vintner,
who drank all himself.

W was a Watchman,
and guarded the door;

X was Expensive,
and so became poor.

Y was a Youth,
  that did not love school;

Z was a Zany,
  a poor harmless fool.

An Alphabet of Nursery Rhymes

Illustrated by Lynne Chapman

A wise old owl lived in an oak;
The more he saw, the less he spoke.
The less he spoke the more he heard:
Why can't we all be like that wise old bird?

a
b
c
d
e
f
g
h
i
j
k
l
m
n
o
p
q
r
s
t
u
v
w
x
y
z

Baa, baa, black sheep,
Have you any wool?
Yes, sir, yes, sir,
Three bags full:
One for my master,
And one for my dame,
And one for the little boy
Who lives in the lane.

a
b
c
d
e
f
g
h
i
j
k
l
m
n
o
p
q
r
s
t
u
v
w
x
y
z

Curly Locks, Curly Locks, wilt thou be mine?
Thou shalt not wash dishes, nor yet feed the swine,
But sit on a cushion and sew a fine seam,
And feed upon strawberries, sugar and cream.

a b c d e f g h i j k l m n o p q r s t u v w x y z

Dance to your daddy,
My little babby,
Dance to your daddy,
My little lamb;
You shall have a fishy
In a little dishy,
You shall have a fishy
When the boat comes in.

Early to bed and early to rise,
Makes a man healthy, wealthy and wise.

a b c d e f g h i j k l m n o p q r s t u v w x y z

For want of a nail, the shoe was lost,
For want of a shoe, the horse was lost,
For want of a horse, the rider was lost,
For want of a rider, the battle was lost,
For want of a battle, the kingdom was lost,
And all for the want of a horseshoe nail.

a
b
c
d
e
f
g
h
i
j
k
l
m
n
o
p
q
r
s
t
u
v
w
x
y
z

Girls and boys come out to play,
The moon doth shine as bright as day;
Leave your supper and leave your sleep,
And come to your playfellows in the street.
Come with a whoop, come with a call,
Come with a good will or not at all.
Up the ladder and down the wall,
A halfpenny roll will serve us all.
You find milk and I'll find flour,
And we'll have a pudding in half an hour.

Hey diddle diddle,
The cat and the fiddle,
The cow jumped over the moon;
The little dog laugh'd
To see such sport,
And the dish ran away with the spoon.

a
b
c
d
e
f
g
h
i
j
k
l
m
n
o
p
q
r
s
t
u
v
w
x
y
z

66

a
b
c
d
e
f
g
h
i
j
k
l
m
n
o
p
q
r
s
t
u
v
w
x
y
z

I had a little nut-tree, nothing would it bear
But a silver nut-meg and a golden pear;
The King of Spain's daughter came to visit me,
And all for the sake of my little nut-tree.

Jack and Jill
Went up the hill,
To fetch a pail of water;
Jack fell down,
And broke his crown,
And Jill came tumbling after.

a b c d e f g h i j k l m n o p q r s t u v w x y z

Kit be nimble,
Kit be quick,
Kit jump over
The candlestick.

Little Jack Horner
Sat in a corner,
Eating a Christmas pie;
He put in his thumb,
And pulled out a plum,
And said, What a good boy am I!

a b c d e f g h i j k l m n o p q r s t u v w x y z

70

Mary had a little lamb
Its fleece was white as snow;
And everywhere that Mary went
The lamb was sure to go.
It followed her to school one day,
Which was against the rule:
It made the children laugh and play,
To see a lamb at school.

$$\frac{16}{\frac{4}{12}}$$

$$\frac{20}{\frac{12+}{32}}$$

$13 \div 2 =$

a
b
c
d
e
f
g
h
i
j
k
l
m
n
o
p
q
r
s
t
u
v
w
x
y
z

a b c d e f g h i j k l m n o p q r s t u v w x y z

Nauty Pauty Jack-a-Dandy
Stole a piece of sugar candy
From the grocer's shoppy-shop,
And away did hoppy-hop.

One misty, moisty morning
When cloudy was the weather,
There I met an old man
Clothed all in leather;
Clothed all in leather,
With cap under his chin.
How do you do, and how do you do,
And how do you do again?

Pat-a-cake, pat-a-cake, baker's man,
Make me a cake as fast as you can:
Pat it and prick it, and mark it with B,
And toss it in the oven for baby and me.

a
b
c
d
e
f
g
h
i
j
k
l
m
n
o
p
q
r
s
t
u
v
w
x
y
z

Queen of Hearts
She made some tarts,
All on a summer's day;

a b c d e f g h i j k l m n o p q r s t u v w x y z

The Knave of Hearts
He stole those tarts,
And took them clean away.

75

a b c d e f g h i j k l m n o p q r s t u v w x y z

Ring-a-ring o'roses,
A pocket full of posies,
A-tishoo, a-tishoo!
We all fall down.

Sleep, baby, sleep,
Thy father guards the sheep;
Thy mother shakes the dreamland tree
And from it fall sweet dreams for thee,
Sleep, baby, sleep.

a
b
c
d
e
f
g
h
i
j
k
l
m
n
o
p
q
r
s
t
u
v
w
x
y
z

This little pig went to market,
This little pig stayed at home,
This little pig had roast beef,
And this little pig had none.
And this little pig cried, Wee, wee, wee!
All the way home.

Up and down the City Road,
In and out the Eagle,
That's the way the money goes,
Pop goes the weasel!

Violante, in the pantry,
Gnawing at a mutton bone;
How he gnawed it,
How he clawed it,
When he found himself alone.

a
b
c
d
e
f
g
h
i
j
k
l
m
n
o
p
q
r
s
t
u
v
w
x
y
z

Wee Willie Winkie runs through the town,
Upstairs and downstairs in his nightgown,
Rapping at the window, crying through the lock,
Are the children in their beds?
For now it's eight o'clock.

80

a
b
c
d
e
f
g
h
i
j
k
l
m
n
o
p
q
r
s
t
u
v
w
x
y
z

X shall stand for playmates Ten;
V for Five stout stalwart men;
I for One, as I'm alive;
C for Hundred, and D for Five;
M for a Thousand soldiers true,
And L for Fifty, I'll tell you.

a b c d e f g h i j k l m n o p q r s t u v w x y z

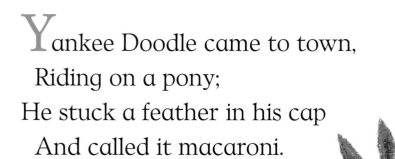

Yankee Doodle came to town,
  Riding on a pony;
He stuck a feather in his cap
  And called it macaroni.

Z, Y, X and W, V,
U, T, S, and R, Q, P,
O, N, M, and L, K, J,
I, H, G,
F, E, D,
And C, B, A.

a
b
c
d
e
f
g
h
i
j
k
l
m
n
o
p
q
r
s
t
u
v
w
x
y
z

A, B, C, D, E, F, G,
H, I, J, K, L, M, N, O, P,

L, M, N, O, P, Q, R, S, T,
U, V, W, X, Y, Z,

X, Y, Z, sugar on my bread,
If you don't like it,
It's time to go to bed!

The Christmas Alphabet

Illustrated by Mary Claire Smith

A

Angel

B

Bows

C

Candle

D

Decorations

E

Envelope

F

Fun

G

Goose

H

Holly

a b c d e f g h i j k l m n o p q r s t u v w x y z

I

Ice skating

J

Jingle bells

K

King

L

Lights

M

Mistletoe

N

Nativity

O

Oranges

P

Presents

a b c d e f g h i j k l m n o p q r s t u v w x y z

Q

Queen

R

Reindeer

S

Stocking

T

Tree

U

Unwrap

V

Visitor

W

White

X

Xmas

91

a
b
c
d
e
f
g
h
i
j
k
l
m
n
o
p
q
r
s
t
u
v
w
x
y
z

Y

Yule-tide log

Z

Zither

merry christmas

The End